CEREMONIAL MUSIC
FOR ORGAN

Oxford University Press

Music Department 44 Conduit Street London W1R 0DE

FANFARE
on 'Gopsal'

DAVID WILLCOCKS

Brillante ♩ = 84

poco ten.

Manuals

ff

Gt. to Mixtures + Full Sw.
Ped. to 8', 16' Reeds

Pedal

poco ten.

fff

poco ten.

Duration 1¼ minutes

Printed in Great Britain

OXFORD UNIVERSITY PRESS, MUSIC DEPARTMENT, 44 CONDUIT STREET, LONDON, W1R 0DE

Pomposo

Tuba (*or* Ch. *or* Gt. 4', 8' Reeds)

legato

Molto largamente

Full Gt.

Tuba (*or* Gt.)

+ 32'

† If tuba and 32' reed are not available, the last bar should be played thus:

The tune, by Handel, on which this fanfare is based, is generally associated with the hymn 'Rejoice, the Lord is King.'

FANFARE
on 'Old 100th'

PETER HURFORD

Duration 1 minute

† Distribution between the hands is at the player's discretion.

Ceremonial music for organ

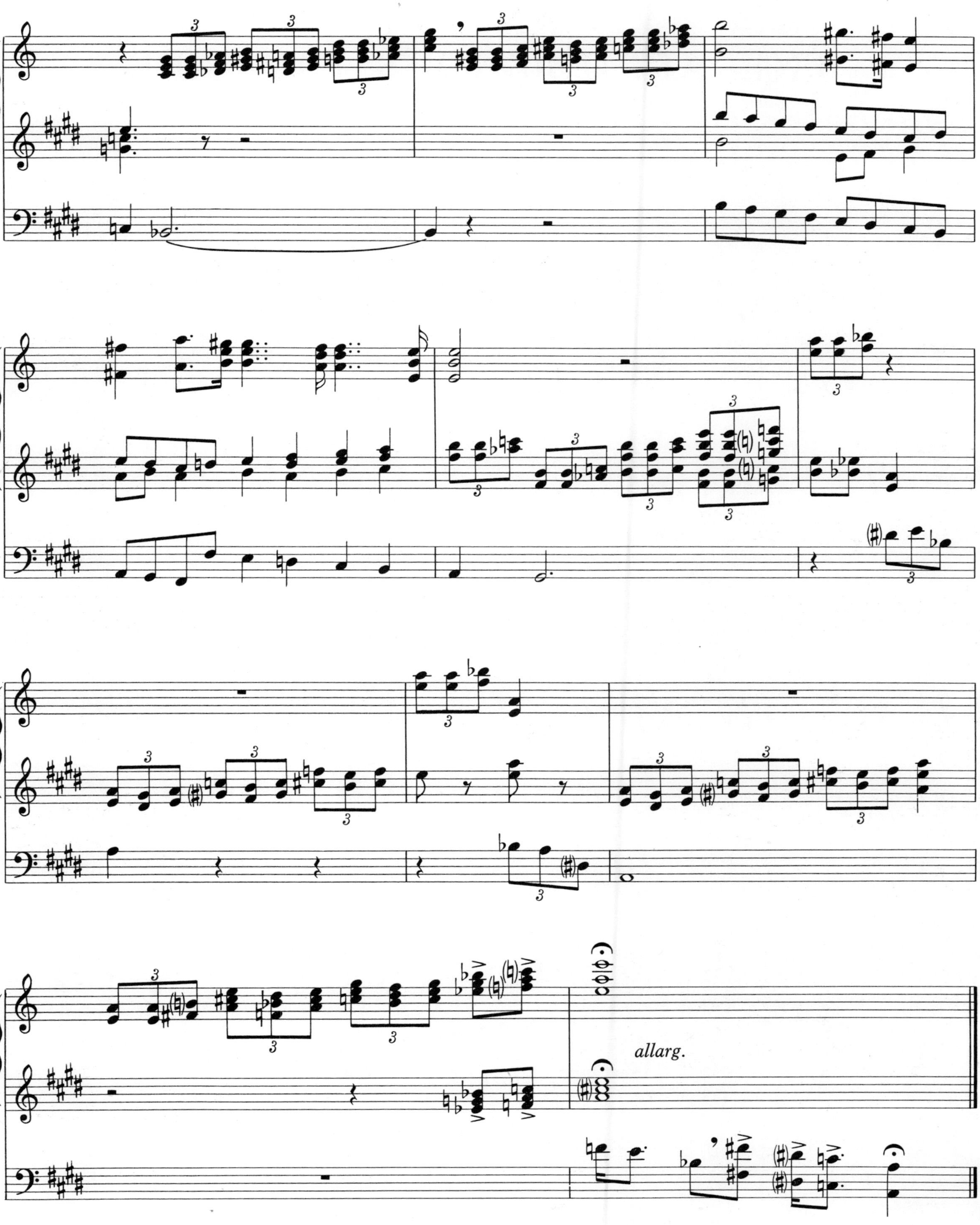
allarg.

to W. M. Coulthard

THE ARCHBISHOP'S FANFARE

FRANCIS JACKSON

Duration 1 minute

This fanfare was written in 1961 for the enthronement of the Most Reverend
F. D. Coggan as Archbishop of York in York Minster.

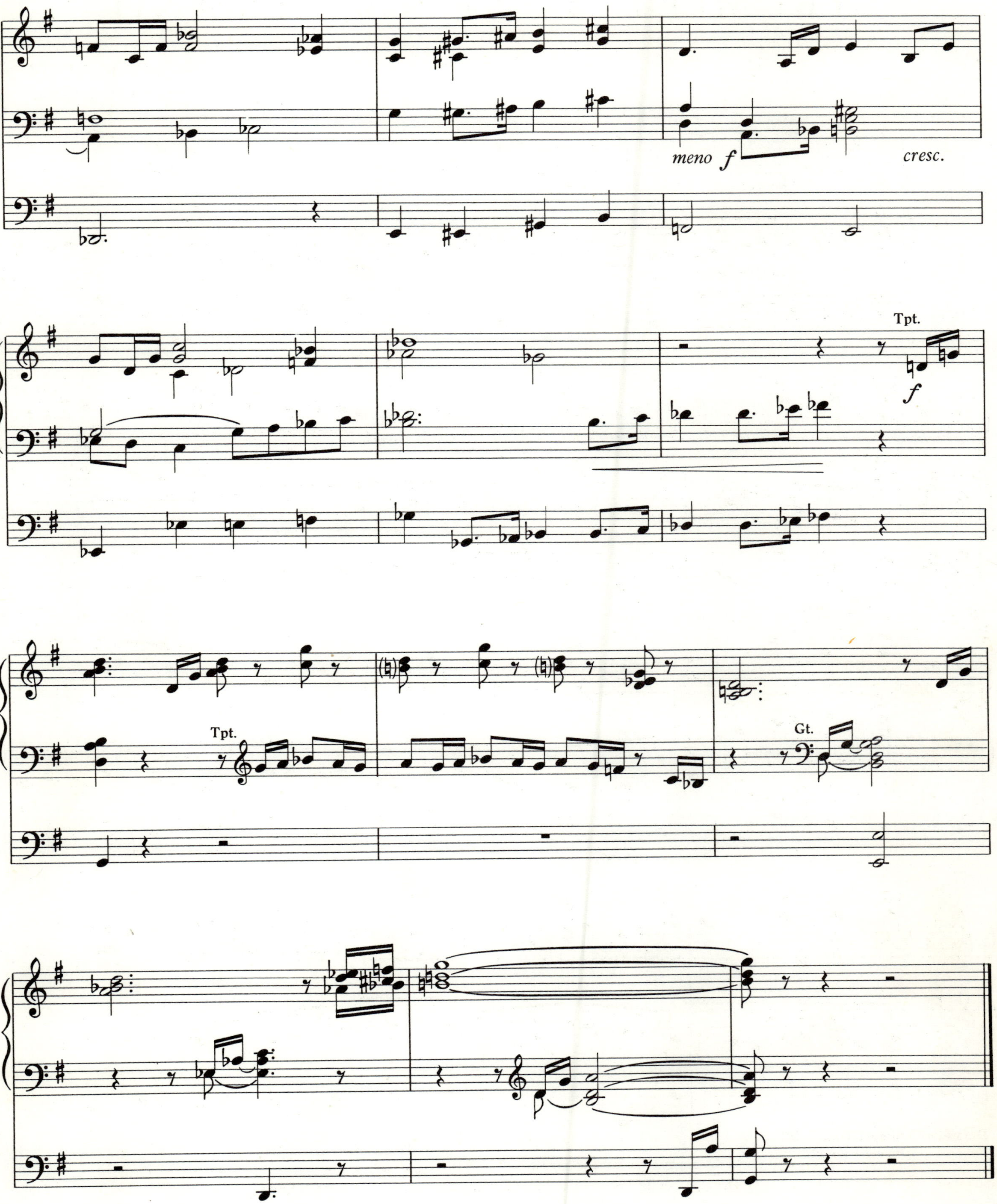
meno f
cresc.
Tpt.
f
Tpt.
Gt.

TRUMPET TUNE and ALMAND

HENRY PURCELL ~
Francis Jackson

Durations: Trumpet Tune 1′ 10″
Almand 1 minute

In the original the first and similar bars are written
The repeat of the first strain is editorial. Ornaments should be interpreted thus:

Ceremonial music for organ

The last and similar bars originally

Ceremonial music for organ

10

ALMAND

This *Almand* (Z643), from Purcell's first harpsichord suite, is also found, with an added variation, as a separate piece.

8'+4'+1⅓'

(Trumpet Tune D.C.)

Ceremonial music for organ

The Prince of Denmark's March

JEREMIAH CLARKE ~
Peter Hurford

Duration 1¾ minutes

The trumpet tune (r.h.) and bass are as they appear in the earliest known printed edition—*A Choice Collection of Ayres for the Harpsichord or Spinett . . .* (John Young, London, 1700). Suggested variants (p. 12) and additions (p. 13) to the tune are printed small except in the final 8-bar reprise, where they are incorporated in the text. All phrasing is editorial. Ornaments should be interpreted as follows:

Note that a trill oscillates for only the first half (or two thirds) of its written value.

To Mixtures

Ceremonial music for organ

TRUMPET VOLUNTARY

JOHN STANLEY ~
David Willcocks

Duration 2¾ minutes

★ There is no repeat in the original. (Modern edition in facsimile: 30 Voluntarys ed. Denis
Vaughan, O.U.P.). Crossed slurs, and symbols in brackets or printed small are editorial.

Ceremonial music for organ

† ♩ = 𝅗𝅥 in original.

Ceremonial music for organ

† The '5ths' are original.

Ceremonial music for organ

Processed and printed by
Halstan & Co. Ltd., Amersham, Bucks., England